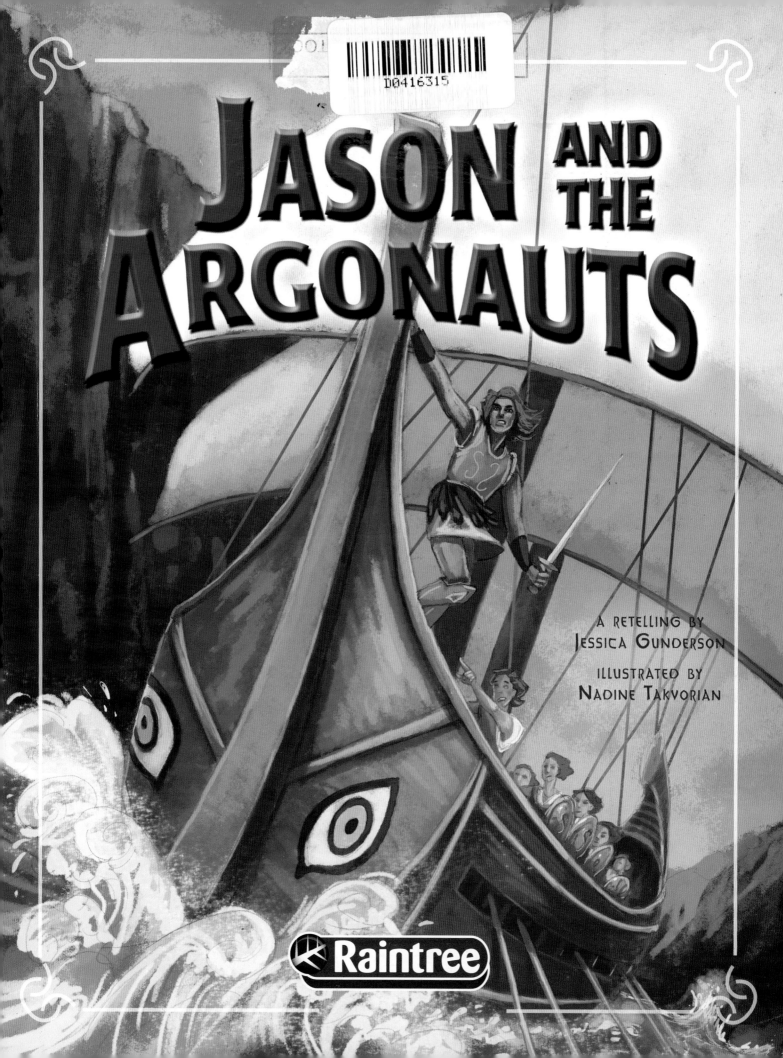

JASON AND THE ARGONAUTS

A RETELLING BY
JESSICA GUNDERSON

ILLUSTRATED BY
NADINE TAKVORIAN

Raintree

CAST OF CHARACTERS

ORACLE: priest or priestess through whom a god or goddess speaks

PELIAS: king of Iolcos

HERA: goddess of marriage, known for her jealousy

POSEIDON: god of the sea

JASON: nephew of King Pelias and captain of the *Argo*

ARGOS: builder of the *Argo*

ARGONAUTS: the *Argo's* crew

ZETES AND CALAIS: winged brothers

PHINEUS: king of Salmydessus. He was blind but could see into the future.

HARPIES: winged female creatures

AEËTES: king of Colchis and keeper of the Golden Fleece

APHRODITE: goddess of love

MEDEA: daughter of Aeëtes and a sorceress

WORDS TO KNOW

COLCHIS ancient kingdom east of the Black Sea

IOLCOS ancient Greek city

MOUNT OLYMPUS home of the Olympian gods

SACRIFICE offering to a god

SORCERESS woman who practises magic

THE ORACLE WARNED KING PELIAS

of Iolcos, "Beware of the man with one sandal."

Pelias knew he had not been a good king. He had stolen the throne from his half-brother. He often ignored the gods, especially Hera. Even so, to beware of a man with one sandal? The king laughed. Who would wear only one sandal?

The king began preparing a sacrifice for Poseidon, the god of the sea. Hera was furious when she heard the king gave offerings to Poseidon but not to her. She knew she must destroy King Pelias. Then she had an idea.

Far from the palace, the king's nephew Jason was sleeping. Hera leaned over him and whispered into his ear, "The throne is rightfully yours."

When Jason woke, he was angry. The throne was his! He set off on the long journey to King Pelias' palace.

When Jason reached the River Anaurus, he saw an old woman begging to be carried across. "I'll carry you," Jason offered.

He lifted the woman on to his back. She looked light, but she was very heavy. Halfway across the river, Jason stumbled and fell. When he stood up, the old woman was gone. So was his sandal.

Above him, the goddess Hera giggled. She shook herself out of her old woman's disguise, holding the sandal in her hand.

King Pelias of Iolcos was sitting on his throne admiring his riches, when his nephew Jason appeared. The king stood to greet him, then saw that Jason wore only one sandal. He stared at Jason thoughtfully. "What would you do if you knew someone meant to harm you?" he asked.

Jason scowled at the king. What sort of greeting was this? "I'd send him to fetch the Golden Fleece," he answered, surprising himself. He did not realize that an invisible Hera was whispering in his ear again.

King Pelias smiled. The Golden Fleece! He had heard about the fleece. It was the pure-gold coat of a magical ram. It hung in Colchis, a faraway land, and was guarded by a dragon that paced, snarled, and never slept. "Come to think of it, I have always wanted the Golden Fleece," Pelias answered. "I command you to fetch it for me!"

Jason knew there was no point in arguing. "I will bring you the Golden Fleece if you promise to hand over the throne," he said.

Pelias nodded. "I promise," he agreed. He knew there was no way Jason could succeed at such an impossible task.

Jason called upon the shipbuilder Argos to build him a ship. He named it the *Argo*.

Then he gathered fifty of the strongest and bravest men in Greece to sail to Colchis with him. Among them were fighters, sailors, athletes, and musicians. The flying brothers Zetes and Calais also joined in.

Jason and his men, known as the Argonauts, set sail under a bright sun. The quest for the Golden Fleece had begun.

Jason and the Argonauts sailed for many years in search of Colchis. They often stopped for food and rest. Each new stop held a new adventure. As the ship sailed further from home, however, Jason worried that they would never find Colchis.

They sailed on until they landed at Salmydessus. Here, they met a blind, starving king named Phineus. Gruesome winged creatures hovered above the king, licking their lips.

"These vicious Harpies steal my food every time I sit down to eat," Phineus moaned.

"We will rid you of the Harpies," Jason promised, "if you tell us the way to Colchis."

Phineus agreed, and Zetes and Calais, the winged brothers, quickly flew up into the sky. They chased the Harpies so far away they never returned.

Phineus told Jason the way to Colchis. He also warned him about the Clashing Rocks. The giant cliffs crashed together and destroyed any ship that tried to pass through. "Release a dove," Phineus told him, "and if it returns unharmed, the passage is open. If not, you must turn back."

Jason and the Argonauts sailed on, and soon they heard the thunderous clashing of rocks. Fog hung like thick curtains over the cliffs. Jason released a dove high into the air. Then he waited.

At last, the dove returned and Jason and the Argonauts sailed through the cliffs to Colchis.

Aeëtes, the king of Colchis, was not pleased when he heard of the strangers' arrival. He knew there was only one reason anyone would travel so far – to capture the Golden Fleece.

The king frowned when Jason presented himself. "I will not allow you to take my fleece," he told Jason, "unless you earn it."

"How can I do that?" asked Jason.

The king pointed outside. In the grounds of his palace, two enormous bulls were kicking and bucking. Flames sprayed from their mouths.

"You must harness these bulls and attach a plough to them, without getting burned," the king said.

Jason nodded bravely, but inside he shivered.

"Then you will plough until you uncover the magical dragon's tooth buried in the palace grounds," the king continued.

Jason nodded again, watching the kicking bulls breathe fire at him. *How will I ever make it out of Colchis alive?* he wondered.

The goddess Hera had been hiding behind the curtains, watching King Aeëtes speak to Jason. She knew Jason needed help. She flew away and called upon Aphrodite, the goddess of love.

Aphrodite followed Hera to Colchis. As the two goddesses hovered over the land, Aphrodite saw a young woman walking along the river towards the palace. Aphrodite swooped closer to watch her.

The young woman was Medea, the king's daughter. Aphrodite smiled and aimed her bow, shooting an arrow of love into Medea's heart.

At that moment, Medea turned and looked at the palace. She saw Jason standing at the window. Feelings of love pulsed through her heart.

Medea knew what her father had in store for him. If she did not help Jason, he would surely die.

That night Medea sent messengers to tell Jason to meet her by the river. As she watched him approach, she felt the stirrings of love all over again.

"I can help you harness the bulls," she told him.

"You?" he asked with a laugh. "How?"

"Don't laugh," Medea said. "I am a sorceress." She held out a small vial. "Rub this potion over your body, shield, and sword. It will prevent the fire from burning you."

"And what of the dragon's tooth?" Jason asked.

"When you dig up the tooth, armed men will spring from the ground," Medea answered. "Throw stones at them. They will become confused and attack each other instead."

"What can I give you in return?" Jason asked.

Medea smiled. "You can take me as your wife," she said.

"If I succeed, I will marry you," Jason agreed.

The next day, all the people of Colchis gathered to watch the spectacle.

In his room, Jason rubbed Medea's potion all over his body, sword, and shield. He filled a small bag with stones. Then he strode out into the palace grounds. He waved at the crowd, the king, and Medea. He even waved at the bulls, who were charging towards him, breathing fire.

As the bulls neared, Jason pretended to dodge the flames. The crowd cheered. Then he marched straight over to the bulls and began dancing in their fire. The heat did not bother him.

The people were amazed at Jason's bravery. Their cheers grew louder.

Only King Aeëtes sat silent and angry. Next to him, Medea covered her smile with her hand.

The bulls grunted and kicked, confused, as Jason looped harnesses over their heads.

King Aeëtes grew angrier still. "But he won't be prepared for the armed men," he consoled himself.

Jason led the bulls around the grounds. The plough dug deep into the earth. Then he heard a clank as the plough hit the dragon's tooth. He uncovered the tooth and lifted it from the ground, holding it up for the crowd to see. He kept one hand on the bag filled with stones.

Dozens of armed men suddenly sprang from the ground, their armour and weapons full of soil. Jason hurled one stone, then another, and another.

The men stopped, confused. "Why did you throw a stone at me?" one man shouted to another.

"Why did you throw a stone at *me*?" the man answered, raising his weapon.

All the armed men started shouting and charging at each other. Jason leapt out of the way to let them fight.

With the fighters occupied, Jason strode over to the surprised and angry king. "I have done what you asked," he said. "Now you must give me what I want: the Golden Fleece!"

"Never!" cried King Aeëtes.

"Never!" Medea cried in agreement. As Jason turned away, she whispered to him, "Meet me at the fleece. Hurry!"

The fleece hung shimmering and golden from the trees. A dragon larger than the *Argo* itself paced around, hissing and spitting.

How will I fend off this gigantic dragon? Jason wondered.

Medea laughed. "I'm a sorceress, remember?" she said. She began chanting and the dragon calmed down. Medea sprinkled a potion over its eyes. The dragon slowly dropped off to sleep.

Jason gathered up the Golden Fleece. He and Medea ran over to the ship where the Argonauts waited, oars ready.

King Aeëtes and his men followed the *Argo*, but their ships were not fast enough. Jason and the Argonauts sailed into the horizon, bound for Iolcos. His quest for the Golden Fleece having been victorious, Jason was sure he would soon be king.

When Jason returned to Iolcos, he marched straight to King Pelias' palace. Pelias saw Jason and turned pale. He had never expected Jason to return, especially not with the Golden Fleece.

"I am king now," said Jason.

"Never!" cried the king. "Get rid of him!" Pelias' guards forced Jason out of the palace and warned him to never come back.

When Medea learned what the king had done, she was very angry. She wanted Jason to be king, and herself to be queen. She would make Pelias pay.

Medea told Pelias' daughters that she had a potion to make their father young and strong again. First, though, they had to slice him into pieces. She demonstrated by sprinkling her potion on the cut-up body of an old ram. It immediately sprang to life, young and strong.

The princesses chopped up their father. After he was in pieces, Medea threw away the potion and left Pelias for dead.

Now no one stood between Jason and the throne.

However, Medea had not foreseen the anger of the frightened people of Iolcos. As punishment for the murder of their king, they forced Jason and Medea to leave the country, warning them never to return. Jason would never become king.

Jason's quest was not fulfilled as he had planned. However, there was one person who was pleased with the turn of events. High above the clouds on Mount Olympus, the goddess Hera smiled. Pelias had received the ultimate punishment for ignoring her. Hera had got her revenge.

www.raintreepublishers.co.uk
Visit our website to find out
more information about
Raintree books.

To order:
☎ Phone 0845 6044371
📄 Fax +44 (0) 1865 312263
💻 Email myorders@raintreepublishers.co.uk

Customers from outside the UK please telephone +44 1865 312262

Raintree is an imprint of Capstone Global Library Limited, a company incorporated
in England and Wales having its registered office at 7 Pilgrim Street, London, EC4V 6LB
– Registered company number: 6695582

Text © Picture Window Books 2012
First published in the United Kingdom in 2012
The moral rights of the proprietor have been asserted.

We would like to thank Terry Flaherty, Professor of English at
Minnesota State University for his advice and expertise.

Editors: Shelly Lyons and Vaarunika Dharmapala
Designer: Alison Thiele
Art Director: Nathan Gassman
Production Specialist: Sarah Bennett
The illustrations in this book were created with watercolours, gouache, acrylics, and digital technology.

ISBN 978 1 406 24306 2 (paperback)
16 15 14 13 12
10 9 8 7 6 5 4 3 2 1

British Library Cataloguing in Publication Data
A full catalogue record for this book is available from the British Library.